White Fang

adapted for young readers
from the original text by Jack London

illustrated by Van Gool

Part 1 The Wild North *3*
Chapter 1 A Special Wolf Cub 5
Chapter 2 Grey Beaver 13
Chapter 3 Learning to hate 23

Part 2 A New World *31*
Chapter 4 Mr Scott 33
Chapter 5 Learning to love 39
Chapter 6 A Great Guard 47

© Creation, script and illustrations: A.M. Lefèvre, M. Loiseaux, M. Nathan-Deiller, A. Van Gool
Text adapted for young readers by Duncan Crosbie
First published and produced by **Creations for Children International**, Belgium. www.c4ci.com
This edition published by BPI, India Pvt Ltd
16, Ansari Road, Darya Ganj, New Delhi - 110 002
Tel.: +91-11-2328 4898 • 2327 6118 • Fax: +91-11-2327 1653
Email: bpipl@bpiindia.com • bpiindia@airtelbroadband.in
All rights reserved
Printed in Singapore

Part one
The Wild North

CHAPTER ONE

A Special Wolf Cub

In the most northern part of Alaska is a wild, savage country. During winter, the days are very short and the sun hardly shines. It gets so cold that the rivers freeze over. Those hunters brave enough to go out use them as roads. Only the toughest hunters venture into this hostile land. However, the American Indians often set up their winter camps in the forests, putting up their teepees around great fires.

These fires protected them from the cold and also from bears, lynx and wolves.
There were many wolves in the wild and at this time of year they were more dangerous than ever. When the wolves are hungry, they will fight amongst themselves, or even attack humans! One winter morning One Eye the Wolf set out to hunt for food for his family.

His female companion was sheltering under some rocks. Recently she had become less enthusiastic about joining One Eye in his hunt for food. The little cave satisfied her, and a few days later she gave birth to a litter of splendid wolf-cubs.

One Eye was very proud of his fine family, but he had to work hard. As the five cubs were still young, their mother could not leave them. It was up to One

Eye alone to go hunting. Every day he would roam far and wide in search of food, and at first he always managed to catch something. But one evening One Eye did not return to the cave. 'Something terrible must have happened to him,' thought the she-wolf. He must have fought a lynx, half mad with hunger! She realised that she would have to hunt for herself now… Often she returned empty-handed to the cave. As the days passed the wolf cubs grew thin and

weak, and soon four of them closed their eyes for ever. The remaining cub had always been the sturdiest. For many days the wolf cub stayed inside, scared of the world outside. But one day, he began to stagger towards the daylight! How excited he was when he discovered what lay outside his lair! Excitedly he ran and rolled in the snow.
He wanted to explore and often got into trouble!

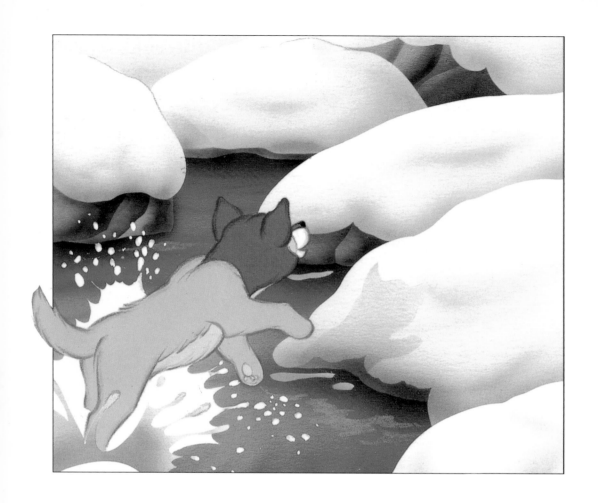

Suddenly he saw something sparkling through the trees. It was the river. Not realising the danger, the wolf cub leaped into the river. The current pulled him along. With a surge of strength he managed to fight his way to the bank…

Over the next few days the cub explored the forest. He loved to go hunting. What was more exciting than catching small animals and birds? He was not cruel but he knew the tough law of the wild: eat or be eaten… Soon the wolf cub was doing his best to catch larger game. One day he even came to his mother's rescue. As she returned to the cave, she was suddenly attacked by a lynx… The young cub didn't hesitate and leaped on the lynx's back. Once the lynx was laid low, the she-wolf lovingly licked her son's wounds…

CHAPTER TWO

$\mathcal{G}$rey Beaver

Every day the wolf cub roamed further from the cave. One day an Indian teepee was set up not far from his cave. Five strange animals came towards him, walking on two legs! These men were a group of hunters from the nearby Indian camp. They hunted herds of reindeer to sell their skins at the white men's fort. Although they did not attack or threaten him, the cub could not move for terror.

Just then his mother came rushing into the clearing. To the cub's surprise she didn't run away but sniffed the air for several moments! The she-wolf immediately lay down on the ground before the men, wagging her tail…

'Kiche!' exclaimed one of the men.
'You're right, Grey Beaver, it's really her!'

One of the Indians, Grey Beaver, had recognised the she-wolf. Several years ago there had been a terrible famine and she had left the Indians. She ran off into the forest, where she had met the wolf One Eye. 'So, this is your son,' said Grey Beaver. 'What a nice little fellow! And what strong white teeth he has. We'll call you White Fang!'

Grey Beaver called to Kiche, who followed him at once. White Fang trailed along behind. They

returned to their camp. The cub was introduced to a new way of life, among the dog-team…

The other dogs were very jealous of White Fang, and never missed a chance to bite or snap at him. His worst enemy was Lip-lip, the boldest of the team's puppies. He always wanted to fight White Fang, and the other young dogs in the camp followed his example.

Lip-lip's expression of dislike towards White Fang grew more intense every day! Luckily, he grew large enough to defend himself. The wolf cub was not only getting stronger, he also used his brains well. When one day Lip-Lip was chasing White Fang, the wolf cub sought shelter and comfort with his mother. The she-wolf growled so fiercely at the little dog that he stayed away from White Fang for many days afterwards…

So White Fang grew used to life in the Indian camp. He trotted around the camp, curious to learn about everything. One morning the Indians decided to move camp further north, so they could follow the herds of reindeer.

It took a whole morning to fold the teepees and to settle each family's load on the sledges.

Seeing everyone bustling around, White Fang felt unhappy. He wished that he could go back and live free again in the woods. So he ran away into the forest and walked straight on for a long time. But when night was falling, he felt very lonely. He kept looking over his shoulder… he wanted to return to the camp! Finally, he made up his mind, turned round and retraced his tracks! The next morning he found the camp at last.

White Fang expected to see his mother again but Grey Beaver had decided otherwise. Kiche was given to Three Eagles, the Indian chief of a neighbouring tribe…

When White Fang saw the she-wolf getting into the canoe of her new master and disappearing, he knew he would never see her again. He howled for a long time…

Although he missed his mother, White Fang soon learned to survive on his own. His upbringing in the harsh nothern wilderness had made him strong and cunning. In a fight he knew to leap straight for the throat, which is an animal's weakest spot. But he also knew to run away if attacked by a stronger animal.

He learned always to respect those stronger than himself and to make those weaker respect him!

CHAPTER THREE

Learning to hate

The years passed, and White Fang grew into a great strong wolf. Grey Beaver decided that it was time to train him to pull one of the sleds. He placed White Fang at the head of the team.

The leader's place is of course the hardest one to hold onto: all the dogs of the team were jealous, and treated the leader as an enemy…

At first White Fang tried to turn round and fight the dogs, but Grey Beaver whipped him until he learned to run instead.

No sled ever moved so fast! For the dogs were all trying to catch White Fang, and he was careful to keep ahead of them...

One summer, the Indians travelled down the river

to the town of Fort Yukon. White Fang's life was about to take a new turn…

Grey Beaver and some other Indians took with them a great pile of furs and made them into coats and hats. The people of Fort Yukon were rich, and paid well for these furs. Grey Beaver took White Fang as a guard with him, for he was the strongest one of the pack.

Exploring the city, White Fang was very surprised: he had never seen such people. And they seemed so powerful! They could build fine houses, could buy anything they wanted and wore expensive clothes. There were many of them, more people than White Fang had seen in his whole life. More of them arrived every day, eager to make their fortune in gold…

As he grew used to the town, White Fang noticed that all the men had at least one dog. Grey Beaver was too busy selling his furs, and had little time for White Fang, so the wolf spent his days terrorising the local dogs! There was a sinister man in town who seemed to enjoy watching the dogs fight, and he would often watch White Fang, encouraging him in his fights…

This man was jokingly known as Beauty Smith. In fact he was very ugly, mean and cruel. Beauty Smith was trying to buy White Fang from Grey Beaver. But the Indian refused to sell: 'Never will I sell the best of all my dogs!' But one night Beauty Smith took Grey Beaver to the inn, and filled Grey Beaver's cup to the brim…
Grey Beaver's protests grew weaker and eventually

he sold White Fang for almost nothing!

Beauty Smith kept White Fang chained up. He had decided to organise fights between the wolf and the town dogs. Men would come and place bets with Beauty Smith that their dog would win. 'This is the easiest way to earn some money,' he thought.

White Fang, ill-treated, grew into a very fierce animal! He always won, and Beauty Smith collected

a pile of money every evening. Although it was White Fang who won him the money,
Beauty Smith kept on treating him cruelly…

Part two

A New World

CHAPTER FOUR

Mr Scott

Within several weeks there were no more dogs left
for White Fang to fight. Beauty Smith decided to go
to another town. He kept the poor wolf in a tiny
cage, only letting him out to fight. White Fang had
become so wild with rage, that he killed all the dogs
brought to fight him. Beauty Smith laughed to
himself. During the fights he encouraged White
Fang: 'Get him! Attack! Go for the throat!'

Then one day, a new dog arrived, a bulldog, with a ferocious reputation... As soon as the fight began, he leaped at White Fang, and knocked him to the ground.

'Get up, White Fang!' cried Beauty Smith. 'Attack!'
But every time White Fang tried to go in for the kill, the bulldog fought free.

At last the bulldog forced White Fang to the ground, and began to bite him savagely. White Fang was losing the fight and his life… Just then, two men stepped forward and entered the ring. It was Mr Scott and his friend Matt, two well-known engineers in town. They knelt down beside the dogs. Matt used his revolver to prise open the bulldog's jaws, and pulled the two animals apart.

Mr Scott owned the mine and was very powerful in the city. 'We'll look after this poor animal!' said Scott. So Mr Scott and Matt took care of White Fang, and within a few weeks the wounded animal recovered.

'Look!' said Matt to Scott one day. 'Someone has already tamed him. His fur is marked: he used to wear a harness!' Mr Scott realised that White Fang was savage because of the ill treatment he had received from Beauty Smith.

As the weeks passed White Fang grew less fierce. But he still bared his teeth and growled when Scott tried to pat him. 'We will have to tame him again,' said his new master. However, White Fang did his very best when Scott and Matt harnessed him to a sledge.

CHAPTER FIVE

Learning to love

Instead of punishing him, Mr Scott continued to treat White Fang kindly. Soon the wolf realised that Mr Scott meant him no harm, and began to enjoy being cared for.

A few months later, Mr Scott had to leave town. The wolf felt awkward seeing his master packing his luggage… 'Look how unhappy he is!' said Matt. 'He knows you're leaving and he won't eat anything.'

'But I can't take him with me to California!' answered Mr Scott.

On the day Scott was leaving, Matt had to shut White Fang in the barn, where he howled miserably. All the way to the dock, Mr Scott thought about White Fang. White Fang heard the voice of his master as he said goodbye to Matt. As silence fell again, the wolf hurled himself as hard as he could through the window…

Sadly Mr Scott boarded the boat, and walked up to the deck. As he looked down at the gangway, his eyes widened in surprise – for there was White Fang!

'Ok, you win,' murmured Scott and brought White Fang on board. The wolf had been so determined to join his master that he had broken out of the barn!

A few days later White Fang got off the boat in San Francisco. He was terrified. Never had he seen so many people. The streets were so long he could not see the end. Worst of all were the motor cars that rushed past. They smelled terrible, and the noise of their engines was frightening.

When the car pulled up, the busy city was far behind. Scott's family home was a few kilometres outside San Francisco. When Scott greeted his family, White Fang began to growl at the strangers. Mr Scott was so happy to see his family that he took no notice of the wolf. But when his wife ran up to hug him, White Fang thought she was attacking his beloved master and barked furiously. Scott soothed him, trying to make him understand that there was no danger…

White Fang had learned his lesson, and when Scott's parents came to greet him, he stood back, watching curiously.

But there was another difficult moment to come... Suddenly another dog came racing out of the house and jumped to greet Mr Scott!
Furious, White Fang turned on the dog who was

trying to take his master away. Just as he was about to attack he suddenly stopped.

For the dog, named Collie, was female, and all White Fang's instincts told him that he must not attack her. Instead he contented himself with growling jealously whenever she came near Mr. Scott.

CHAPTER SIX

$\mathcal{A}$ Great Guard

As the weeks passed, White Fang got used to living in the great house. He was never violent, but he was never friendly either. The servants, the other dogs and even Scott's wife and children tried to make friends with him, but White Fang simply ignored them. The only friend he wanted was Mr Scott. Wild wolves do not appreciate familiarity!

Soon it emerged that White Fang was not yet completely tamed. Every day he would walk past the hen house, licking his lips hungrily. One day a servant forgot the close the henhouse door…

At once White Fang leaped inside and attacked the poor chickens! They squawked in terror!

Luckily Collie came past, and when she saw what was happening she leaped at White Fang. Not daring to attack her, he ran off back to the house.

When Mr Scott heard the squawks, he ran to the henhouse and punished the wolf severely. 'Lie down!' he ordered. White Fang lay down on the

ground obediently. He would never touch another chicken…

White Fang did not have to do much. But he was useful to Mr Scott's family: he was given the important task of watching over his master and protecting him from all dangers. Mr Scott would often go out riding horseback in the woods and White Fang always went with him.

One morning the horse was startled by a hare and reared up. She lost her balance and fell to the ground, throwing Mr Scott from her back. Mr Scott groaned with pain, but could not stand up. White Fang tried to pull his master to his feet, but Scott only managed to whisper: 'Go to the house and fetch help!'

White Fang hesitated a moment… but at last he flew off as swift as an arrow to Scott's house…

White Fang raced into the house, and found Mrs Scott in the kitchen. He stopped before her, looking at her, then looking back towards the woods. Suddenly she realised something was wrong.

'Where is your master?' she cried. The wolf howled, then turned and began running back towards the trees. Mrs Scott called to the servants, and they followed the faithful wolf.

The horse quickly recovered, but Mr Scott had to stay several weeks in bed.

White Fang would not leave his side until he was up and about. The wolf's love and loyalty had won over everyone in the house. 'That animal's getting more and more like a dog every day!' smiled Mrs Scott.

Most surprisingly, Collie began to look at White Fang in a different way. In fact White Fang tried hard to please her... They were often seen together, walking through the trees outside, or laying side by side on the hearth. It seemed that the wild wolf had won the heart of the proud Collie!

The following spring, Collie gave birth to six beautiful puppies. They all looked like their mother, except one, who had a shaggy grey coat like a wolf!

Mr Scott and his wife laughed to see White Fang and his family playing together, and Mr Scott was always glad that he had saved the wolf from his savage life!